Letterland

Phonics Activity Book 3

My name is

CW00552421

Let's learn about...

ng sh ch

th wh ph

a_e ai ay

About Letterland

Letterland is an imaginary place where letters come to life! The friendly Letterland characters help children to easily understand the sound and shape of letters – one of the key skills needed when learning to read and write.

Simple stories about the Letterland characters explain letter sounds and shapes, so that confusion over similar looking letters is avoided and children are motivated to listen, think and learn.

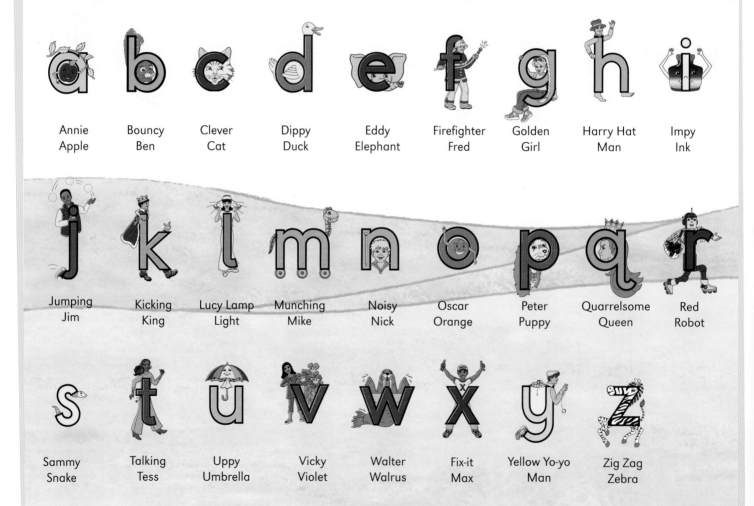

| Annie Apple | Bouncy Ben | Clever Cat | Dippy Duck | Eddy Elephant | Firefighter Fred | Golden Girl | Harry Hat Man | Impy Ink |

| Jumping Jim | Kicking King | Lucy Lamp Light | Munching Mike | Noisy Nick | Oscar Orange | Peter Puppy | Quarrelsome Queen | Red Robot |

| Sammy Snake | Talking Tess | Uppy Umbrella | Vicky Violet | Walter Walrus | Fix-it Max | Yellow Yo-yo Man | Zig Zag Zebra |

For more information, including a pronunciation guide for all the letter sounds, see: **www.letterland.com**

How to use this book

Letterland stories give child-friendly reasons why, when certain letters come together, they make a completely new sound. On each page, read the Spelling Story and talk about the Letterland characters and the reasons for their change of sound. Your child will quickly discover how easy it is to remember the new sound just by learning the story reason for it. For more fulsome versions of the stories, you might like to look at our *Phonics Touch and Spell* book or the titles *Beyond ABC* and *Far Beyond ABC*.

Note: A 'digraph' is two letters representing one sound. e.g. **sh**op

Study the pages together with your child. Each time start by reviewing the previous digraphs, to practise their sounds before focusing on the next pages. The aim is for your child to respond without hesitation with the correct sound for each digraph.

Stickers

Award stickers as you go along. You may also like to start a Digraph scrap book using the character stickers from *Phonics Activity Books* 3 to 6. Look out for words to collect under each of them. Where you see this icon, you will need stickers to complete the exercise.

Skills covered include:
- phonemic awareness
- decoding skills
- word building
- reading for meaning
- sentence completion

It is important to use this *Phonics Activity Book*:
- when children are not tired
- when there are no background distractions
- for short periods of time
- with plenty of praise and encouragement.

Left-hander

Finger tips 4cm
from tip of pencil

Paper side edge

30°

Table edge

Paper side edge

20°

Table edge

Right-hander

Finger tips 2cm
from tip of pencil

Noisy Nick and Golden Girl

When Noisy Nick and Golden Girl sit together in a word they are so happy they make a si**ng**ing sound, '**ng**'.

1. Fill in the spaces with **ng**. Read the words. Join them to the picture that matches.

si_ng_

ha___

ri___

di___ do___

4

2. Can you hear Noisy Nick and Golden Girl together in the sentences below? Ring them.

Ding dong!
Kicking King
rings the bell.

We can sing a
long song!

Bing, bong, bang!
Nick is on
the drums.

5

Spelling story

Whenever Sammy Snake starts to hiss loudly behind Harry Hat Man's back, Harry turns back and says, '**sh**!' because he hates noise.

1. Draw a pathway to connect Sammy Snake and Harry Hat Man to the words that contain their sound. Write the words in the spaces. Cross out the other pictures.

shoe

2. Read the two words below the picture. Circle the
word that matches the picture.

ship   shut

shack   shin

axes   ash

kick   cash

3. Read the sentence that goes with this picture twice.
Then write it on the line below.

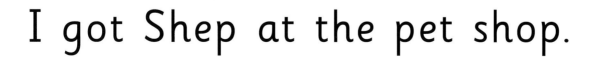

I got Shep at the pet shop.

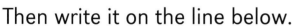

Clever Cat and Harry Hat Man

When Clever Cat sits next to Harry Hat Man, his hairy hat tickles her nose so she almost always sneezes, 'ch!'

1. Read the sentences and look at the picture clues. Fill in the spaces using the **ch** words below.

checks	chicks	chops

He _____ on the _____ .

He catches the _____ .

Then he _____ some logs.

2. Draw a line around all the **ch** words in the word search below. They go across and down.

c	h	t	o	s	h	n
h	s	c	l	c	a	c
a	c	h	i	p	s	e
i	x	o	h	w	n	o
r	j	p	c	h	i	n
c	h	i	c	k	l	p

chick

chin

chips

chop

3. Can you find one more
ch word in the grid?
Copy it on to the lines.

_____   _____   _____   _____

1. Read the two words beneath each picture.
Circle the word that matches the picture.

sing   ring   bang   hang   king   wing

2. Fill in the spaces with **ch** or **sh**. Read the words.
Then join them to the pictures.

___ in         ___ op

___ op         ___ ell

fi ___         ___ ick

The Letterlanders are coming together to build words! Say their sounds, then blend them together to read the words.

sh i p

shi p

ship

ch o p

cho p

chop

Talking Tess and Harry Hat Man

Talking Tess knows Harry Hat Man hates loud noises so whenever there are thunder clouds overhead she hurries to his side saying, '**Th**ere, **th**ere.'

1. Use the words below to fill in the sentences.

This   Shep

_____ is _____ and me.

that   She

_____ naps in _____ shed.

Talking Tess and Harry Hat Man

When two thunder clouds bump overhead both Tess and Harry think it is too loud. They stick out their tongues and whisper, '**Th**under, **th**under, **th**under!'

1. Read the six words. Then choose four of them to fill in the blanks below the pictures.

| thin | path | maths | thick | chin | bath |

_____

_____

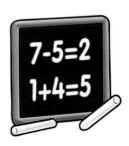

_____

_____

2. Choose the correct words below to complete these sentences.

| thick | path | thin | chin |

Ed has _____ legs.

The duck has _____ legs.

3. Finish the words below and read the sentence.

She is

___inking.

4. Finish the words with **th** and read the sentences.

__ is man chops logs on __ e pa __ .

A mo__ on a clo__ !

Walter Walrus and Harry Hat Man

When Walter Walrus finds Harry Hat Man standing ahead of him with his tall hat on Walter cannot see. So he splashes his hat off. Harry Hat Man is too surprised to speak.

1. Read the two words beneath each picture. Circle the word that matches.

whiff   whoff

whack   whap

whozz   whizz

whisk   whosk

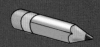

2. Look at the picture. Then read the sentences. Colour the star next to the sentence that best matches the picture.

When will he drink?

When will he get up?

When will he sing?

In a few words Harry Hat Man gets annoyed and cries, '**Wh**o do you think you are?' and throws a bucket of water over Walter Walrus.

1. Read the sentences. Fill in the gaps using the words below.

| whole |
| Whose |

1. A _____ plum.

2. _____ hat is this?

ph

Spelling story

Harry Hat Man makes Peter Puppy happy by taking his **ph**otogra**ph**.
Harry Hat Man laughs quietly with his teeth on his lips, so his usual 'hhh' sound becomes a 'fff' sound.

1. Match the sentence to the correct picture.

A photo of a trophy.

An elephant on the phone.

The alphabet is on this trophy.

2. Draw a line around all the **ph** words in the word search below. They go across and down.

b	r	s	d	t	q	t
s	p	h	o	n	e	r
c	u	v	l	w	p	o
g	r	a	p	h	h	p
e	d	f	h	g	o	h
i	j	k	i	m	t	y
p	h	i	n	e	o	h

phone

trophy

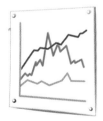

graph

dolphin

photo

1. Read the sentences and look at the picture clues. Fill in the spaces using the **th**, **wh** and **ph** words below.

thing	What	dolphin	that

_____ is that _____?

I think _____ is a fin.

It is a _____ !

2. Draw a funny creature in the box. Then answer the question.

What is that thing?

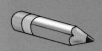
3. Can you hear Walter or Harry saying their sound in the words below? Copy the words on to the lines in the correct box.

whisk	whom	which	whose

 when

_____

_____

_____

 who

_____

_____

_____

4. What is Talking Tess trying to say? Fill in the spaces with **th**, **wh** or **ph** to find out.

A tro__y! __anks! __at is fantastic. __at fun!

Mr A and Silent Magic e

Silent Magic **e** shoots back its Magic Sparks over one letter to make Mr A appear and say his name, '**A**!' in lots of words.

1. Read the two words beneath each picture. Circle the word that matches the picture.

hat   hate

plan   plane

cap   cape

can   cane

2. Cross out the words that do not belong in the sentence.

The | male / mill |  has a thick | man / mane .

3. Write a word for each picture.

_____ _____ _____ _____

4. Finish the sentence using the words below. Cross out the words that do not fit.

| Kate cape grapes cake cane |

_____ tops the

_____ with

_____ .

When Mr A and Mr I go out walking, Mr A does all the talking. He just says his name, '**A**!' while Mr I remains silent, as he looks out for robots.

1. Read the two words beneath each picture. Circle the word that matches the picture.

train   tram   ran   rain   tail   tall

paint   pan   rain   rail   sail   snail

2. Read the sentences. Then colour the star next to the matching picture.

It's raining on the train.

He's painting in the rain.

The chain is on the snail.

3. Can you find Mr A and Mr I out walking in some words below? Underline them.

This dog has a plain chain on his neck. His name is Kane. He wags his tail.

Spelling story

When Mr A and Yellow Yo-yo Man go out walking, Mr A does all the talking. He just says his name, '**A**!' while Yellow Yo-yo Man remains silent, as he looks out for dangerous robots.

1. Draw a pathway to connect Mr A and Yellow Yo-yo Man to the words that contain their sound. Write the words in the spaces. Cross out the other pictures.

_____

tray

_____

_____

_____

_____

2. The Letterlanders are playing. Fill in the spaces with the words they might say today.

hay   day   play   tray   Sunday

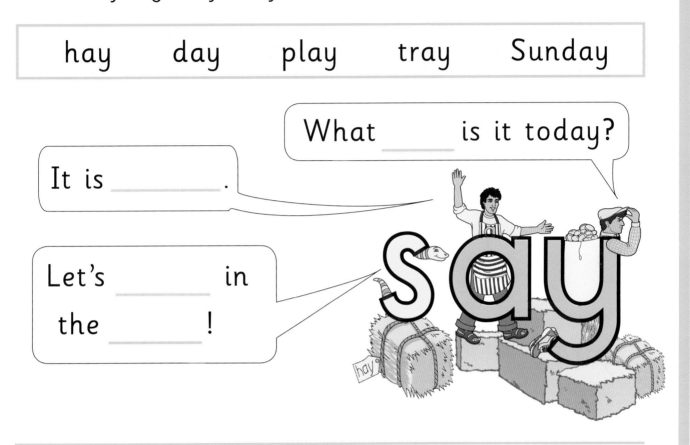

What _____ is it today?

It is _____ .

Let's _____ in the _____ !

3. Mr A and Yellow Yo-yo Man are going on holid**ay**. Circle all the **ay** words on their postcard.

Friday 9th May

Today we ate a takeaway!

To

_____
Write your name on the line.

Let's review - a_e, ai, ay

1. Circle the **a_e** word that rhymes in each row.

lake

cat

snake

ant

gate

hat

bat

skate

rake

ink

cake

sack

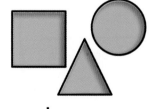

shapes

grapes

ship

shop

28

2. Mr A and Yellow Yo-yo Man like to go out walking at the end of every day. Write **ay** on the lines to finish the days.

Mond _____   Tuesd _____

Wednesd _____

Thursd _____   Frid _____

Saturd _____   Sund _____

3. Finish the sentence using the **a_e**, **ai**, and **ay** words below. Cross out the word that does not fit.

tray	train
cake	chain

The _____ is on a _____ in the _____ .

29

Sticker time!

Read the sentences and put your stickers in the correct places to complete the picture.

Put a chick on the path.
Put a chick in the hay.

Where are the chicks?

Put a chick on top of the cake.
Put a chick in the train.

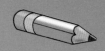

4. Can you find Silent Magic **e** making Mr A appear in the sentence below? Underline them.

Mr A waves as the cat makes a cake.

5. Can you find the words below that contain Mr A saying his name? Underline the Vowel Men.

This dog hates the rain and trains.